Silly Shakespeare

A Midsummer Night's Dream

PAUL LEONARD MURRAY

with help from

WILLIAM SHAKESPEARE

Alphabet
PUBLISHING

ISBN 978-1-948492-71-3

For permission requests or discounts on class sets and bulk orders contact us at:

Alphabet Publishing
1204 Main Street #172
Branford, CT 06405 USA

info@alphabetpublishingbooks.com

www.alphabetpublishingbooks.com

For performance rights, please contact Paul Murray at paulplaying@gmail.com

Interior Formatting and Cover Design by Melissa Williams Design

This book is dedicated to the young people of the original Belgrade English Language Theatre cast of the play (2019) without whom it would have never been written.

Ana Blagojevič
Mina Blagojevič
Manja Jelovac
Pavle Kaucki
Matija Marinkovič
Relja Marinkovič
Milutin Miličevič
Tara Radulovič
Uroš Stojanovič
Nemanja Vasič
Radivoje Vlaškalič

Summary

Written in 1595/96, *A Midsummer Night's Dream* is one of Shakespeare's most performed plays. Our version is very close to the original in terms of plot, characters, and narrative. We have added a short introduction by a narrator and Puck and have combined some of the minor fairy characters into the part of Fairy.

Theseus, the duke of Athens, is preparing for his marriage to Hippolyta, queen of the Amazons, with a four-day festival of entertainment. He commissions his Master of the Revels, Philostrate (who in our version is Puck in disguise), to find suitable amusements for the occasion. Egeus, an Athenian nobleman, marches into Theseus's court with his daughter, Hermia, and two young men, Demetrius and Lysander. Egeus wishes Hermia to marry Demetrius (who loves Hermia), but Hermia is in love with Lysander and refuses to agree. Egeus asks for the full force of the law to fall on Hermia's head if she disobeys her father. Theseus gives Hermia until his wedding to consider her options, warning if she disobeys her father's wishes she could be sent to a convent or even executed.

Nonetheless, Hermia and Lysander plan to escape Athens the following night and marry in the house of Lysander's aunt, some distance away. They make their intentions known to Hermia's friend Helena, who was once engaged to Demetrius and still loves him (even though he dumped her after meeting Hermia). Hoping to regain his love, Helena tells Demetrius of Hermia and Lysander's plan. At the appointed time, Demetrius stalks into the woods after his intended bride and her lover. Helena follows him.

In these same woods are two very different groups of characters. The first is a band of fairies, including Oberon, the fairy king, and Titania, his queen. They have recently returned from India to bless the marriage of Theseus and Hippolyta. The second is a band of Athenian craftsmen (the Mechanicals) rehearsing a play that they hope to perform for the Duke and his bride.

Oberon and Titania are arguing over a young Indian servant boy given to Titania by the prince's mother; the boy is so beautiful that Oberon wishes to make him a servant, but Titania refuses. Seeking revenge, Oberon sends his servant, Puck, to acquire a magical flower, the juice of which can be spread over a sleeping person's eyelids to make that person fall in love with the first thing he or she sees upon waking. Puck obtains the flower, and Oberon tells him of his plan to spread its juice on the sleeping Titania's eyelids.

Having seen Demetrius act cruelly towards Helena, he orders Puck to spread some of the juice on the eyelids of the young Athenian man. Puck sees Lysander and Hermia; thinking that Lysander is the Athenian of whom Oberon spoke, Puck puts the love potion in his eyes. Lysander happens to see Helena upon awaking and falls deeply in love with her, abandoning Hermia.

As the night progresses and Puck attempts to undo his mistake, both Lysander and Demetrius end up in love with Helena, who believes that they are making fun of her. Hermia becomes so jealous that she tries to challenge Helena to a fight. Demetrius and Lysander nearly do fight over Helena's love, but Puck confuses them by mimicking their voices, leading them apart until they are lost separately in the forest.

When Titania wakes, the first creature she sees is Bottom, the most ridiculous of the Mechanicals, whose head Puck has transformed into that of a donkey. After Titania has passed some time doting on the donkey-headed weaver, Oberon (unseen) obtains the Indian boy. Puck spreads the love potion on Lysander's eyelids, and by morning all is well. Theseus and Hippolyta discover the sleeping lovers in the forest and take them back to Athens to be married. Demetrius now loves Helena because of the potion, and Lysander loves Hermia again.

Following the wedding ceremony (unseen), the lovers watch Bottom and his fellow craftsmen perform their play, a fumbling, hilarious version of the story of Pyramus and Thisbe. When the play is completed, the lovers go to bed; the fairies briefly emerge to bless the sleeping couples with a protective charm and then disappear. Only Puck remains, to ask the audience for their forgiveness and approval and to urge them to remember the play as though it had all been a dream[1].

1—The keen-eyed amongst you may notice some direct use of a few original lines/ words, including the final word in each line of Puck's final monologue being the same as the original version.

Playing Style

This version of *A Midsummer Night's Dream*, although reduced to around a one-hour playing time, remains true to the original's plot, characters (with some small exceptions), and structure. When performed, this production should maintain a lively pace and exaggerated style. Although Puck is directed to speak directly to the audience, other characters can follow his lead in order to maintain an intimate feeling between characters and audience. Technically, the production, as with the original, has a very low level of technical requirements. The sets can be very minimal and the costumes simple. A musical score may be used between scenes to cover changes where necessary.

Of course, one of the major differences between this version and the original is the simplification of the text. On some occasions, in performance, you will find the rhyming scheme helpful to the playing, in which case the actors should just 'stand back', enjoy the words and help the audience do the same. On other occasions, the rhyming scheme will seem stifling and restrictive, in which case do not be afraid to improvise a little, add your own occasional lines, or do not emphasise the rhymes so much. Overall, this version should be fun to play and watch. It can be produced with a small budget and should be done 'over the top' which can give you a chance to play with your own ideas of theatricality.

Cast of Characters

FAIRIES

PUCK:	*The servant of Oberon. Very mischievous fairy.*
TITANIA:	*The wife of Oberon and queen of the fairies.*
OBERON:	*The husband of Titania and king of the fairies.*
FAIRY:	*The servant of Titania.*

ATHENIANS/THESEUS' COURT

THESEUS:	*The Duke of Athens, impatient to be married.*
HIPPOLYTA:	*The Queen of an Amazon tribe. Brought back to Athens as a prize of war and is now Theseus's fiancée.*
PHILOSTRATE:	*Theseus' servant (played by Puck in disguise)*
EGEUS:	*Hermia's father and Greek Lord, impatient for his daughter to marry Demetrius.*
HERMIA:	*The daughter of Egeus. Both Demetrius and Lysander are in love with her. But she loves only Lysander.*
LYSANDER:	*Young Athenian aristocrat in love with Hermia.*
HELENA:	*Aristocratic Athenian friend of Hermia's. In love with Demetrius.*
DEMETRIUS:	*Young Athenian aristocrat, former boyfriend of Helena. Now in love with Hermia.*

MECHANICALS

(A group of lower-class craftsmen attempting to put on a play for Theseus' upcoming wedding)

QUINCE:	*The play director*
BOTTOM:	*A joiner, plays Pyramus*
FLUTE:	*Plays Thisbe*
SNUG:	*Plays the lion*
SNOUT:	*Plays the wall*
STARVELING:	*Plays the moon*

Act I

Prologue

CHORUS

(Each actor to take at least one line and address the audience directly)

Good evening. Welcome to the show
Midsummer Night's Dream, I'm sure you all know . . .
It's a famous work by Will the Bard
But his language can be kind of hard

So this evening we will do our best
To simplify old William's text.
As you can hear, we'll speak in rhyme
And cut two hours off the running time.

So for those of you who have an aversion
To seeing Shakespeare in a modern version,
Best go now before we start
To pull this classic play apart.

But for those of you with short attention,
Our show's a really great invention:
Only the highlights and none of the dross².

PUCK
And me, I'm Puck, I'm a fairy, of course.

Now you may not believe that I really exist
Or think fairies and ghouls are just shapes in the mist
But in actual fact, that's not really the case:
I stand here as real as the nose on your face.

With the help of one of Shakespeare's shows
We'll show how you humans we keep on your toes.
Talking of which here's the King and the Queen
But don't worry about me, cos³ I cannot be seen!

2—Bad parts

3—Short for because

SCENE I.

Athens. The palace of THESEUS.
(Enter THESEUS, HIPPOLYTA, *and Attendants)*

THESEUS
Hippolyta, dear, well, here's your new home.
It may not be so fancy but at least it's not Rome.
In Athens we have far more manners and taste
So your beauty and charm will not go to waste.

HIPPOLYTA
Manners and taste? Have you muddled[4] your brains?
You stole me from home, and you keep me in chains.

THESEUS
Oh, don't be like that my dear Amazon queen
It's old-fashioned romance . . .

HIPPOLYTA
. . . it's not, it's obscene!
I have not got a choice but to marry you here.

THESEUS
Then you may as well face it. Crack open a beer.

4—Mixed up, scrambled

(THESEUS *passes* HIPPOLYTA *a beer*)

Philostrate, Philostrate! Where the heck is he now?

(PUCK *enters disguised as* PHILOSTRATE)

PHILOSTRATE
I'm right here, your Highness

THESEUS
. . . There is no need to bow.

PUCK
(*Aside*) Yes, it's Puck here—you knew that—disguised as
   a man
I do this sometimes just to make good my plan.

THESEUS
I'm worried my queen is getting cold feet.
And a little bit drunk. (*To* HIPPOLYTA) Here, love, take a
   seat.
(*To* PHILOSTRATE) This wedding you promise will win
   me her heart?

PHILOSTRATE
Don't you worry 'bout that Lord, I'll just make a start.

(*He exits*)

HIPPOLYTA
How long do I have to sit here like this?

THESEUS
Not long now, dear. Perhaps one little kiss?

HIPPOLYTA

Not likely, you heathen[5], not 'til I am freed.

And even after we're married, it's not guaranteed.

(Enter EGEUS *and* HERMIA*)*

EGEUS

Happy be Theseus . . .

THESEUS

. . . Oh, not you again?

EGEUS

It's my eldest girl, Hermia. She's being a pain.

I told her to marry this upstanding lad:

Demetrius, step forward.

(Enter DEMETRIUS*)*

HERMIA

. . . He's an absolute cad!

EGEUS

Stop lying, my child. He's as sweet as a panda.

HERMIA

But I want to marry this man Lysander.

(Enter LYSANDER*)*

5—Someone who is uncivilized

LYSANDER
We had a few dates and we saw some good bands.

EGEUS
And now she won't do what her father commands.
Please tell her, my Lord. I am wasting my breath
She either gets married or we put her to death.

HIPPOLYTA
I'm with you, dear Hermia. It seems that we women
Around here in Athens don't get an opinion.

THESEUS
(*To* EGEUS) Well, thanks a lot, Egeus, your timing is great.
I know it's a problem, but couldn't it wait?
(*turns to* HERMIA) Now listen, Hermia, it's Demetrius or
    bust
And I'll even let you get married with us.

HERMIA
Well I don't want to die, but this man ain't no fun.

THESEUS
Either marry him, dear, or you'll live as a nun!

EGEUS
Oh, thank you, my Lord. I'm sure she'll agree.

THESEUS
She'd better do, mate . . . Now let's go have tea.

(*Exeunt all but* LYSANDER *and* HERMIA)

LYSANDER
Well, the course of true love in our case is dead,
So I'd better be going, you heard what he said.

HERMIA
Is that it? Not so fast. Are you a man or a mouse?
Let's run off to your Auntie's house.

LYSANDER
That cute little shack on the edge of the wood?

HERMIA
And there we'll get married. You got it?

LYSANDER
Yes . . .

HERMIA
. . . Good!

(Enter HELENA*)*

HERMIA
Oh, hi there, Helena. How are you?
Your hair looks great. Did you do something new?

HELENA
I'm trying to look more serious
To win that man Demetrius,
But whatever I say and whatsoever I do
He has only got eyes for you,
Your eyes, your ears, your mouth, your nose . . .

HERMIA
My head and shoulders, knees and toes?

HELENA
Don't tease me so, it's not a joke.
I'm obsessed with that Demetrius bloke.
I wish I had your gorgeous looks
To get in that man's good books.

HERMIA
All other men, they say you're hot
But Demetrius has lost the plot.[6]
It doesn't matter what I say.
He's waiting for our wedding day!

HELENA
But you love him (*indicates* LYSANDER). Did I get that
    right?

HERMIA
(*nodding*) Which is why we're skipping town tonight.

LYSANDER
Well, actually we leave tomorrow,
But we'll put an end to all your sorrow.

HERMIA
We'll never come back . . .

LYSANDER
. . . I swear it's true.

6—Lost touch with reality

HERMIA
And then he'll only have eyes for you.

(Exeunt HERMIA *and* LYSANDER*)*

HELENA
Oh, Cupid, such a cruel sprite
To land me in this awful plight.
He loved me once: Demetrius.
But Hermia she did ruin us.
And even when he knows their plan
I'm sure he'll never be my man.
He'll follow them into the trees
To catch a peek, but if you please
I'll follow him to enrich my pain
Just to see him go . . . (hopefully) and come back again.

(Exit)

SCENE II.

Athens. QUINCE'S *house.*

Enter QUINCE, SNUG, BOTTOM, FLUTE,
SNOUT, *and* STARVELING

QUINCE
Welcome, lads. I'll make it clear
The reason we are meeting here.
We're here to rehearse and put on a play
For the Duke and Duchess' wedding day.
I've got the cast, I've got the script.

BOTTOM
Oh, please can we get on with it?

QUINCE
Pyramus and Thisbe is the play.
It was a classic of its day.
An epic work of sorrow and joy:
When a boy meets a girl . . .

(Steps forwards holding out his hand)

BOTTOM

(Stepping forwards next to QUINCE, *taking
his hand and smiling)*

... And a girl meets a boy.

QUINCE

>   (*Shocked, dropping* BOTTOM'S *hand*)

Nick Bottom, the weaver ...

BOTTOM
... The best actor by far.

QUINCE
You will play Pyramus ...

BOTTOM
... He means I'm the star!

>   (*As* QUINCE *introduces the cast, they step forwards to
>   acknowledge themselves*)

QUINCE
Francis Flute, bellows-mender, give us a twirl
You will be Thisbe ...

FLUTE
... A soldier ...?

QUINCE
... A girl!
Pyramus' girlfriend ...

FLUTE
... Now that's what I feared,
But I can't play no woman cos I got me this beard.

STARVELING
Your mum's got a beard . . .

SNOUT
. . . and your dad didn't care.

BOTTOM
Just suck in your belly and back-comb your hair.
So, I will be the pyramid.

FLUTE
And I will be the Frisbee.

QUINCE
No! Listen, you twits! It's PYRAMIS AND THISBE!!

QUINCE
Robin Starveling, the tailor . . .

STARVELING

> (*Stepping forwards and addressing* FLUTE)

. . . You're making me swoon!

QUINCE
(*To* Flute) Take no notice my dear, he's (*indicating* STARVELING) cast as the moon!
Tom Snout, the tinker . . .

SNOUT

> (*Laughing and referring to* STARVELING)

. . . The moon? Is that all!

(To QUINCE, *smugly)*

And who am I playing . . .?

QUINCE
(*harshly*) You're playing a Wall.

SNUG
(*upset*) And what about me? I'm always picked last
I know I'm no actor, but I should've been cast.

QUINCE
Snug the joiner, come here and enough of your cryin'
You're playing the part of the dangerous Lion.

SNUG
Has the lion got lines? Sorry I'm boring!

BOTTOM
Yes, he has . . . Peter, tell him . . .

QUINCE
. . . it's nothing but roaring.

BOTTOM
You should roar just like thunder escaping a cloud.

QUINCE
Don't listen to Bottom. You'll scare all the crowd
Just do what I ask and now we'll disperse.
Tomorrow night in the woods we'll meet and rehearse.

(Exeunt all)

Act II

SCENE I.

A wood near Athens.

Enter, from opposite sides, a FAIRY *and* PUCK

PUCK
Hey fairy, what's up? What're you doing round here?
You know it's the shortest night of the year?

FAIRY
Oh, is it? I'm busy, I'm serving the Queen,
The queen of the fairies, you know who I mean.

PUCK
Titania . . .?

FAIRY
. . . That's her, got me jumping through fire
Doing all of the stuff that her heart does desire.

PUCK
I hear what you're saying. My master's the same.

I'm flying all over the world . . .

FAIRY
. . . What's his name?

PUCK
King Oberon . . .

FAIRY
. . . That's my mistress's King
We serve the same family . . . !

PUCK
. . . ain't no big thing.

FAIRY
So you're Puck! You're the sprite, if I'm not mistaken.

PUCK
That's me, my good fairy, and a mischief I'm making.
I'm the wind in your willows, the thorn on your rose.
I'm the draft from the window, the itch on your nose.
But no more my rappin'. You gotta be gone
Cos I'm feelin' my man, my Oberon.

FAIRY
The King's coming here? He may be a charmer
But they had a bust up and she ain't no calmer.

PUCK
I heard him rappin' bout some servant boy
They both want to have him . . .

FAIRY

. . . but he isn't a toy.

Titania comes too, I can feel her in the air.

PUCK

Then I think we should join them but keep out of their
     hair . . .

(Enter, from one side, OBERON, PUCK *immediately joins
him; from the other side,* TITANIA *enters and* FAIRY
immediately joins her)

OBERON

My Titania, my queen with her fairy in tow.

TITANIA

Oh look, there's my husband, let's turn round and go.

OBERON

Wait a minute, you woman: am not I thy King?

TITANIA

But it don't mean a thing if it ain't got that swing

So why are you here? No, don't tell me, I know

Your lover's a star in the Duke's wedding show.

OBERON

Hippolyta? The Amazon queen?

That was ages ago. She meant nothing to me

And what about you with that Theseus dude?

I've been hearing some rumours, and some of them rude.

TITANIA

Rumours and lies are a desperate ploy.

You've been ruining our lives with that manservant boy.

OBERON

He just looks so cute, and I need a new slave.

TITANIA

I promised his mum, who now lies in her grave,

To raise him as mine, and that's what I'll do.

But if you give up your claim, I will hang out with you.

OBERON

That servant kid needs a King, not a Queen.

TITANIA

Then you'd better say bye, cos I'm leaving this scene.

(Exeunt TITANIA *with her* FAIRY)

OBERON

She always thinks she wins the day

But I will not let her get away.

Puck, you know that little flower?

PUCK

The one with the special loving power?

OBERON

You read my mind. I've had a notion

To turn it into a loving potion.

Go pick it now and bring it to me.

PUCK
Faster than a bumble bee!

(Exits)

OBERON
I'll watch Titania when she's a sleeper
And drop the potion in her peeper.[7]
The next thing she sees when morning comes
A lion, a bear, or a donkey's bum
She'll lose control, she'll fawn and dote
Until she gets the antidote
Which I will give as soon as she
Gives the servant boy to me.
Is this her coming? I'll disappear.
Invisible, I'll overhear.

(Enter DEMETRIUS, *with* HELENA *following him)*

DEMETRIUS
How many times do I have to say?
I love thee not so get away.
Hermia's the one I want to wed;
Lysander's the one I will have dead.

HELENA
I love the way you yell at me,
It makes my knees go wobbly.

7—Eyes

DEMETRIUS
Can't you see I hate your guts?

HELENA
The way you talk, it drives me nuts.

DEMETRIUS
Is there anything that I can say
To make your sad face go away?

HELENA
No! My love you'll not reject.

DEMETRIUS
Do you have any self-respect?
I treat you like poop that's under my shoe.
I'm sick when I should look at you.

HELENA
I'm sick when you are not with me.
Come hug me underneath this tree.

DEMETRIUS
I would rather stab a fork in my eye.
Now I'm leaving you here and I hope you die!

(Exits)

HELENA
This may sound cheap and rather sleazy
But you don't get rid of me that easy.

(Exits)

(OBERON appears)

OBERON
I hate to see a woman
So besotted[8] with a cruel man.

(PUCK re-enters)
PUCK
I'm back, my Lord, I got the flower
And all in less than half an hour.

OBERON
I'll find Titania before she's awoke
And you look for an Athenian bloke.

PUCK
In Athens . . . ?

OBERON
. . . No, smarty-pants, here in the wood.
He hasn't been treating his girlfriend so good.
When he sleeps, squeeze the potion deep in his eye
So when he wakes up a 'new' girl he will spy.

(Exits)

PUCK
And fall head over heels and happy ever after?
This midsummer's night's getting dafter and dafter.

8—Deeply in love

SCENE II.

Another part of the wood.
Enter TITANIA, *with her* FAIRY

TITANIA
He always thinks that he knows best.
Sing me to sleep, I need a rest.

FAIRY
Right here, my Queen. Are you sure that's wise?
What of all the prying eyes?

TITANIA
Look around, there's no one near.
Just a five-minute nap, there's no need to fear.

FAIRY
Do I have to sing? My voice is shot.

TITANIA
Yes you do. You're all I've got.

(TITANIA *sits and sleeps upstage centre.* FAIRY *sings,*
reluctantly, to the tune of 'Twinkle, Twinkle Little Star')

FAIRY
Twinkle, twinkle, little queen.

Go to sleep and don't be mean.
Dream your dreams and don't be shy,
Like a fairy in the sky.
Twinkle, twinkle, little queen.
Dreamy, dreamy, dreamy dream!

*(*TITANIA *snores,* FAIRY *exits)*

*(*OBERON *enters and squeezes the flower on*
TITANIA'S *eyelids)*

OBERON
I can't believe that lullaby.
Bad enough to make you cry.
But she's sleeping now so all is cool.
Just wake when you see some fool.

(Exits)

(Enter LYSANDER *and HERMIA, lost, not noticing* TITANIA*)*

LYSANDER
Sorry, Love, I lost the map.

HERMIA
And now I need a little nap
I'll just lie here for 40 winks.

(Lies unknowingly to one side of TITANIA*)*

LYSANDER
And I'll lie next to you, methinks.

HERMIA
No funny business 'til we're wed.
Go and find yourself another bed.

LYSANDER
Absolutely. With you, dear.
I'll just go lie down over here.

(Lies unknowingly to the other side of TITANIA. *Enter PUCK)*

PUCK
Through the forest have I been,
But no Athenian have I seen.
But wait a second, I'll just follow my nose.
A man of Athens: I can tell by his clothes.
And here's his lady, sleeping sound,
On the dank and dirty ground.
Abandoned here without a care.
How could you, man? I wouldn't dare.

(He squeezes the potion into LYSANDER'S *eyes)*

Now when you wake and see her face
You'll be knocked out by her charming grace.
So wake up when I'm long and gone,
I must now go to Oberon.

(Exits)

(Enter DEMETRIUS *and* HELENA, *running, not noticing the sleeping characters)*

HELENA
Slow, my sweet, you're losing me.

DEMETRIUS
That's exactly what I want, you see?

HELENA
You'll leave me here? How cruel a blow.

DEMETRIUS
It's what you deserve, alone I'll go.

(Exit DEMETRIUS)

HELENA
Happy is Hermia, wherever she lies
For she has such attractive eyes.
And I'm as ugly as a stone;
It's no surprise that I'm alone.
I do not blame Demetrius
Cos I am surely hideous.

(Sees LYSANDER)

But who is here? Alive or dead?
Lysander, can you move your head?

LYSANDER

(Awakening. He sees HELENA *and falls in love with her)*

I'll move my head for my desire . . .
That's you, Helena! You're on fire!
Your body's fit, your face it glows.

Where is Demetrius? I'll punch his nose.

HELENA
Oh, save your acts of derring-do
He loves your girl, but she loves you.

LYSANDER
Hermia? An ugly bore,
I won't be seeing her no more
It isn't her, but you I love
You're an angel sent from heaven above.

HELENA
Oh, shut your trap, I won't tell you again
I don't need more abuse from men
Demetrius already makes me sick
I don't need you now taking the mick.[9]
I'm leaving now: but must confess,
I thought you of more gentleness.

(Exits)

LYSANDER
She missed old Hermia lying here.
I loved her once, but now it's clear.
Hermia put some spell on me
And made me see her prettily.
Helena, my darling, wait for me,
You'll be my little honeybee.

9—Slang for making fun of someone, also seen as 'taking the mickey'

(Exits)

HERMIA

(Waking up)

Lysander, Lysander, are you awake?
I just had a nightmare; I still feel the shake.
In the dream you said you'd love . . . Helena?
Just out of the blue, with no explainer.

(Looking around)

Are you still there? I think he is gone!
I'm left in the dark scary wood all alone . . .
It may be a dream, and I'm yet to awake,
I'll go and sort out this awful mistake.

(Exits)

Act III

Scene I.

The wood. TITANIA *unnoticed still asleep upstage*

Enter QUINCE, SNUG, BOTTOM, FLUTE,
SNOUT, *and* STARVELING

BOTTOM
Are we all met? To rehearse in the wood?

QUINCE
It's for Theseus' wedding, so we gotta be good.

BOTTOM
Peter Quince . . .

QUINCE
 . . . Yes, Bottom?

BOTTOM
 . . . Can I have a word?
I'm worried about the thing with the sword
When Pyramus stabs himself under the moon
I think that the girls who are watching will swoon,

And then there is Snug, who is playing the beast.

When the girls see his monster, they will sure need a
    priest.

SNOUT

Our play is so scary, I know what he means.

STARVELING

Can't we get rid of the more graphic scenes?

BOTTOM

No need for that, we can write on a sign

That the sword is not real and that Snug is the Lion.

QUINCE

That's very resourceful, I hear what you say,

But can we get back to rehearsing the play?

STARVELING

I was wondering about the moon and the wall.

How do we get them into the hall?

BOTTOM

The moon will be shining that night I'm certain

So we just have to go and open the curtain

As for the wall, well, I've had an idea

That one of the boys can lay down right here

       (BOTTOM *lays down and demonstrates*)

And hold up his legs . . . then a wall will appear!

QUINCE

Right, thank you. Now all of you get to your places

I'm going to start putting the cast through its paces.

(Enter PUCK *unseen from behind)*

PUCK
What a bunch of country bums are these
Gathered here amongst the trees
So near the place of the fairy queen?
They're staging a play? This has gotta be seen.
And after a little investigation
Maybe some audience participation?

QUINCE
Pyramus, Thisbe, get on the set.

BOTTOM
 Thisbe, you smell like odious sweat.

QUINCE
It's 'odours sweet'! You sound like you scoff . . .

BOTTOM
I heard a noise, it's putting me off . . .

(Exits)

PUCK
I'll go and see what's wrong with him?

(Exits)

FLUTE
Was that part of the play? Is he coming back in?

QUINCE

Yes . . . from where you left off, now give him some room.

FLUTE

I'll meet thee, Pyramus, at Ninny's tomb.

QUINCE

Who are you talking to? Your husband's still out . . .
And it's 'Ninus's tomb . . .'

FLUTE

. . . there's no need to shout!!

(Re-enter PUCK, *and* BOTTOM *with a donkey head)*

BOTTOM

You shout all you like cos your Pyramid's back.

QUINCE

Every man for themselves, it's a monster attack!!!

(Exeunt QUINCE, SNUG, FLUTE, SNOUT, *and*
STARVELING, *screaming)*

PUCK

Bottom's a donkey? Well there's a surprise!

And it's got all his buddies rubbing their eyes.

(aside) Just don't let him know that I changed him like
this.

Cos the fun that is coming you don't want to miss!

(Exit)

BOTTOM

Why did they all run away?

I've still got lots of lines to say!

(Re-enter SNOUT*)*

SNOUT

Oh Bottom, you've changed! What do I see?

BOTTOM

You trying to make a fool out of me?

(Exit SNOUT. *Re-enter* QUINCE*)*

QUINCE

Bottom! You've a hideous change . . .

Rehearsals I must rearrange!

(Exits)

BOTTOM

I see what they're doing, and they don't scare me.

Just a practical joke pretending to see . . .

Something changed on my person, but I will not rage.

I'll keep myself calm by singing on stage.

(Sings)

Oh birdy, birdy, tweety tweet

With little legs and yellow feet . . .

TITANIA

(Waking up and seeing BOTTOM*)*

What angel wakes me from my flowery bed?
It's a mortal man with a funny-shaped head.

BOTTOM

(Sings)

Oh bumbly, bumbly, bumbly bees
With hairy legs and furry knees.

TITANIA
Oh gorgeous beast, you sing like a dove.
I do believe I have fallen in love.

BOTTOM
You really think I have a good voice?

TITANIA
... But I'll take your body if given a choice.

BOTTOM
A choice is no choice in affairs of the heart.

TITANIA
Now there's a rare thing; both handsome and smart!

BOTTOM
I should really go now cos you've gone a bit scary.

TITANIA
You're not going nowhere till I'll make you a fairy!
You'll never die, you'll always be.
Living in this wood with me.
Fairy, fairy . . .

(Enter FAIRY*)*

FAIRY
... Did you call?

TITANIA
Who is the fairest of them all?

FAIRY
Whatever you say, ma'am, you know I'll agree.
But before you go dating, I wish you'd ask me.

TITANIA
It's your job to grant every wish, every whim.

FAIRY
I don't know what she sees in him!

TITANIA
Stay with me Adonis, just give it a shot.

BOTTOM
Well put it like that I don't see why not.

(Exeunt all)

SCENE II.

Another part of the wood.
(Enter OBERON)

OBERON
I wonder if Titania has opened her eyes
And what is the first living thing that she spies?

(Enter PUCK)

And as if by magic and right on cue.

PUCK
You won't believe what I'm going tell you.
So I'm back in the trees and I'm hearing a noise.
And it turns out to be some old country boys
Rehearsing a play for the Duchess' wedding.
I think you've worked out where this story is heading . . .
The ugliest one was a bit of a bum
So picking him would be the most fun.

OBERON
So what did you do to this ignorant fool?

PUCK
I changed up his head for that of a mule!
His mates ran off with girly squeals

Then Titania woke up and fell head over heels!

OBERON
That's so much better than I ever desired
And the Athenian man . . .?

PUCK
. . . he was ever so tired.
He didn't feel pain when I put in the potion
And the girl was right there, so the plan is in motion!

(OBERON *and* PUCK *hide as* HERMIA
and DEMETRIUS *enter)*

OBERON
There he is now of whom we speak.

PUCK
That may be the woman, but I don't know that freak!

DEMETRIUS
Just to say it won't be fun
Living the rest of your days as a nun.

HERMIA
Get away from me, you murderous swine.
You've taken out that man of mine.
We slept last night in a clearing (apart),
And when I woke, he'd broken my heart.
He would never leave me just like that.
Now tell me where's the body at?

DEMETRIUS

If he were dead, I'd cheer and shout
But I don't know what you're talking about.

HERMIA

Are you torturing me just for your sport?

DEMETRIUS

May I offer you moral support?

HERMIA

Keep your murdering hands off me,
And tell me where the body be ...

DEMETRIUS

I'm sure he's not dead, I saw no blood
He's just gone for a walk around the wood.

HERMIA

But this wood's so scary and so black
Promise me he's coming back.

DEMETRIUS

If I could promise this to thee,
Tell me, Herm, what's in it for me?

HERMIA

To never see my face again ...
Seriously, girls, I've had it with men.

(Exits)

DEMETRIUS

Now she's upset, was it something I said?

Better not follow, I'll stay here instead

And have myself a little nap

I'm really not that bad a chap!

(Lies down and sleeps)

OBERON

Well there you go, surprise, surprise . . .

You've put the juice in the wrong man's eyes.

Instead of making a wrong love right,

You've messed up our Lysander's sight.

PUCK

Don't flip your wig, it's just a tease

I'll give this guy a little squeeze.

OBERON

Just leave the drug . . . that should be clear!

And go and bring Helena here . . .

PUCK

What does she look like? Is she a stunner?

OBERON

Just bring her back here, and don't do a runner

And while you're gone, I'll prepare his eyes

For the moment when your girl arrives.

Just don't mess up . . .

PUCK

. . . You're pretty frightening!

I'll bring her back, as quick as lightning.

(Exits)

OBERON

(Squeezing the potion into DEMETRIUS' *eyes)*

Flower of this purple dye,

Hit the apple of his eye.

And when Helena he does meet

She will sweep him off his feet.

(Re-enter PUCK*)*

PUCK

Oh, clever Puck did Helena find

But Lysander's following close behind

Now some fun we'll get to peep.

OBERON

Just keep it down, he's still asleep.

PUCK

But if he wakes, we'll have some fun.

OBERON

Just stand by me and keep it shtum[10]

(Again OBERON and PUCK *hide as* LYSANDER *and* HELENA
    enter)*

10—Silent

LYSANDER
I really don't know what to do.
I never loved anyone more than you.

HELENA
You should say this to Hermia's face.
I do not want to take her place.

LYSANDER
I don't know what came over me.
I was lying to her . . .

HELENA
 . . . Now you're lying to me!

LYSANDER
I love you and Demetrius don't,
And I'll marry you cos I know he won't.

DEMETRIUS

(Waking up and seeing HELENA*)*

Helena, goddess, nymph, divine!
Tell me, when will you be mine?
Your blessed face, your golden hair,
Let me be your cuddly bear.

LYSANDER
Demetrius you are just too mean
Hermia's your girl, we all have seen.
Go be with her, you desperate rake,
And leave us two, our love to make.

DEMETRIUS
Keep your Hermia; I was wrong
I loved her once but now it's gone.
Now it's clear and no more muddle,
Can I have a little cuddle?

HELENA
I thought you were both noblemen
But now I'll have to think again.
You overlook my tears of grief
And pick on me without relief.

LYSANDER
I know that love can be unkind
But you're so cute it blows my mind.

DEMETRIUS
It blows mine more, you're very plucky
And I'm not saying that just to get lucky.

(Re-enter HERMIA*)*

HERMIA
Finally, I end my quest
And in your manly arms I'll rest.

LYSANDER
Unhand me now, you desperate tart.
This girl here now has won my heart.

HERMIA
Is that why on the grassy hillock

You left me sleeping like a pillock[11]?

LYSANDER
I woke, I left; you woke, you cried.
Now, can't you see I'm occupied?

HERMIA
At the very least I admire your candour.

LYSANDER
(*Indicating* HELENA) Meet the next Mrs Lysander.

HERMIA
I saw you not eight hours ago
And now you love this little . . .

HELENA
. . . Oh!
The three of you are in cahoots
To make me tremble in my boots.
Hermia, in your evil mode
You've torn apart our sister's code
Have you forgot when we were young,
Dancing, skipping, having fun?
Making dolls from leaves and flowers,
Having girly chats for hours?

HERMIA
I remember every single year
But trust me, I'm not guilty here.

11—A stupid person, British slang

HELENA
How else do you explain these blokes,
If not for some elaborate hoax?
I may not have myself a guy
But you shouldn't want to make me cry.
All three of you do joke with me.

HERMIA
The points you make, I just don't see . . .

HELENA
Oh, very smart, just carry on.
Let's see how long this joke can run.
The knowing winks, the little nudges,
In the end our gods will judge us.
I go now to avoid this curse.
To live? To die? Or . . . something worse.

DEMETRIUS
You are the sunshine of my life.

LYSANDER
Go find yourself another wife.

HELENA
Just stop the joke . . .

HERMIA
. . . Lysander, still!

DEMETRIUS
If she won't stop you, then I will.

LYSANDER
Wild horses couldn't stop me, dear.

DEMETRIUS
I love you more than dogface here!

LYSANDER
Bring it on then, lowly fool.

DEMETRIUS
Let's go and have ourselves a duel.

HERMIA
Lysander, no. You've lost your mind?

LYSANDER
Go away, you troll . . .

HERMIA
 . . . Oh, that's unkind.

LYSANDER
Let's go and fight beside the lake.

DEMETRIUS
(*To* HERMIA) Don't trust him! He's a rattlesnake.
(*To* LYSANDER) I'll head that way and you'll not come.
Stop staring at my woman's bum.

LYSANDER
(*To* HERMIA) Don't touch what you cannot afford.

HERMIA
Your cruel words have struck a chord.

When did our love disappear?

LYSANDER
Shut up and just get out of here.

HERMIA
You joke . . . ?

HELENA
. . . Of course, and you do too.

DEMETRIUS
(*To* LYSANDER) You wanna pop[12]?

LYSANDER
Of course I do.

DEMETRIUS
You dirty rat . . .

LYSANDER
. . . You smelly skunk.

DEMETRIUS
You dirty dog . . .

LYSANDER
. . . You ugly punk.

HERMIA
You're serious! What did I do?
Did last night not mean naught to you?

12—Slang for punch

LYSANDER
I don't know how to say this plainer:
I hate you and I love Helena!

HERMIA
(*To* HELENA) You stole his heart. I don't know how . . .

HELENA
You're blaming me?? You little cow!

HERMIA
Call me little again and I'll come over there
And wipe off your make-up and mess up your hair.

HELENA
Oh gentlemen, don't let my sis
Make such cruel threats as this.
I know with me you're making sport
But please do make her come up short.

HERMIA
My height again . . . !

HELENA
. . . It's my mistake
The mick I did not mean to take.
It's true I pulled out all the stops
To get Demetrius in the copse.
And followed him, my man to see,
But he was very cruel to me
I'm tired of love and all its passions.
Just please let me go back to Athens.

HERMIA
What's keeping you . . .?

HELENA
. . . A foolish heart . . .

HERMIA
. . . for Lysander . . . ?

HELENA
. . . Not that fart!

LYSANDER
Be not afraid, my dinky-doo,
Hermia will not injure you.

DEMETRIUS
Even if she did her best
You'd never pass my manly chest.

HELENA
Thank you, boys. That's good to know.
Her threats to me are very low.

HERMIA
My height again! Her face I'll splatter . . .
Let me go boys, let me at 'er.

LYSANDER
You're pretty tough for such a shorty.

HERMIA
Shut your face . . .

DEMETRIUS
. . . Stop being naughty.
(*To* LYSANDER) You're defending a girl who loves you not.
So drop her or I'll show you what's what.
And stop taking Helena's side
And shorty here now cast aside.

LYSANDER
Hermia thinks I've lost the plot,
So let's go fight for Helen's lot.
Follow me into the wood.

DEMETRIUS
Follow you! This will be good!

(*Exeunt* LYSANDER *and* DEMETRIUS)

HERMIA
Stay right there, you poison shrew
All this mess is cos of you.

HELENA
You may be tougher in a fray
But my longer legs can run away.

(*Exeunt HELENA and HERMIA*)

PUCK
An argument and four-way fight.
What a lovely summer's night.

OBERON
You like this horror in the wood?

PUCK

It's just like being in da hood.

My work round here should be applauded.

Just what the fairy doctor ordered.

A little human chaos ploy

To keep your mind off the servant boy.

OBERON

You put the juice in the wrong guy's eyes.

PUCK

Yes, that came as a bit of a surprise.

But listen, boss, it ain't all bad,

Look at all the fun we've had.

OBERON

You've made a mess; now make it right.

You have to go and stop this fight.

Use your magic fairy powers

To keep them running round for hours

By all means, go and have some fun.

But in the end when it is done,

Have them lying in the clover.[13]

PUCK

(*Jokingly*) Alive or dead . . . ?

OBERON

. . . Oh, Puck, give over!

When the boys do lie . . . asleep!

13—Variation of being 'in the clover', in a good situation

To Lysander carefully creep
And it may not be a big surprise

PUCK
Pop the drug in his mince pies?

OBERON
And when they wake all this will seem
Like . . .

PUCK
. . . A midsummer night's dream?

OBERON
And back to Athens they will go
And forget about your horror show.
Then after that, I see my queen.

PUCK
The donkey-lover, don't you mean?

OBERON
I'll give her a little squeeze of joy
And then I'll get the servant boy.
We'll stop all our games before they're dafter.

PUCK
And they'll all live happy ever after?

OBERON
That's the plan. Now don't be shy.

PUCK
Faster than a butterfly!

(Exit OBERON*)*

Up and down and all around,
I'll run them both into the ground . . .
I'll play not one Greek but play two
It's easy for me . . . it's what I do.

(PUCK *hides as* LYSANDER *enters from the right)*

LYSANDER
Come and show your cowardly self.

PUCK (AS DEMETRIUS)
(hiding) I'm ready to fight, you puny elf.

LYSANDER
I'm on my way, stay where you are.

PUCK (AS DEMETRIUS)
Just follow my voice, I'm not that far.

(Exit LYSANDER *left, as following the voice.* PUCK *changes
his hiding place as* DEMETRIUS *enters right)*

DEMETRIUS
Lysander, you big chicken poop.
I think I'm walking in a loop.

PUCK (AS LYSANDER)
Big talk for one who's always lost.
Come over here and prepare to be bossed.
I'll roast you like a leg of pork.

DEMETRIUS
Say that to my face, you dork.

PUCK (AS LYSANDER)
I will; just find my dulcet tones.

DEMETRIUS
I'll cook your flesh and grind your bones!

(Exit left. Re-enter LYSANDER *right)*

LYSANDER
A two-hour run at a pretty good pace,
I feel like I'm on a wild goose chase.
I hear his voice. It calls me on.
But when I get there, he is gone.
And now it's dark and I feel woozy;
I think I'll have a little snoozy.

(Lies down upstage right)

I'll find him when the dawn it breaks
And win Helena, whatever it takes!

(Sleeps)

(PUCK changes his hiding place once more as DEMETRIUS
enters right, not noticing LYSANDER*)*

PUCK (AS LYSANDER)
What's wrong? You scared to feel my force?

DEMETRIUS
I'm not scared, just need a horse.
He dare not stand, and meet his fate.
And now it's getting rather late.
Where are you now, you little blighter?

PUCK (AS LYSANDER)
I'm over here where it's a wee bit brighter.

DEMETRIUS
The night it comes, and day has gone.
I feel a migraine coming on.
I'll kick his butt when the sun does rise
But until then I'll rest my eyes.

(Lies down and sleeps upstage left. Re-enter HELENA, *not
noticing* LYSANDER *or* DEMETRIUS)*

HELENA
Back at school, I'll tell my class.
They'll never believe what's come to pass.
But I'll never get back to town tonight,
And to stay awake here will give me a fright.
I'll sleep it off and tomorrow we'll see
What the spirits have in store for me.

*(Lies down and sleeps upstage left without
noticing* DEMETRIUS)*

PUCK

(Reappearing)

Three victims down, just one to go.

I've had them all rush to and fro.

And here she comes, here's number four.

Hermia's time to lie and snore.

Thrills and spills we all have had.

Your Puck, he is a clever lad!

(PUCK hides. HERMIA re-enters downstage, not noticing the three sleepers)

HERMIA

I've never been so bruised and battered,

My heart and my nerves are both quite shattered

Alone in life and in this wood.

Perhaps I'll sleep? I think I should.

(Lies down and sleeps upstage right without noticing LYSANDER)

PUCK

(Reappearing)

All our lovers on the ground

Among the trees all safe and sound:

And just to make sure I got the right Greek,

I'll have myself a closer peek.

The other juice did get his goat

So now he gets the antidote.

(Squeezing the juice on LYSANDER'S *eyes)*

And when he wakes, he'll get to spot
That Hermia's there and he'll think she looks hot.
Demetrius will love Hel just like he does now,
And they'll forget the worst of this night somehow.
Their love will be reciprocated
And we'll head to the wedding for which we've all waited.

(Exits)

Act IV

SCENE I.

The same. LYSANDER, DEMETRIUS, HELENA, *and*
HERMIA lying asleep

Enter TITANIA *and* BOTTOM; *and* FAIRY *attending;*
OBERON *behind unseen*

TITANIA

Come, sit with me upon this bed

And let me stroke your furry head.

Like ivy, I will wrap my arms

Around your hairy jug-like[14] charms.

The willow weeps no more than I

To see the vision in my eye.

The mighty birch, the lark, the oak,

The strength of these are but a joke.

You are the one, you have no peers:

No-one can match your marvellous ears.

14—Cockney rhyming slang for ears

BOTTOM
Where's the fairy . . . ?

FAIRY
. . . Here am I.

BOTTOM
I have an itch above my eye.

TITANIA
Then scratch it, Fairy, with a smile.

FAIRY
I'll always go that extra mile.

TITANIA
And when you're done bring him some lunch.

FAIRY
A bale of hay . . . ?

TITANIA
. . . A little bunch.

FAIRY
Of course, my queen. I'll leave tout suite[15]
To bring your mule a little treat.

(FAIRY *exits*)

TITANIA
To bring my what? Too late, she's gone

15—The English version of *tout de suite* which is French for right now

Let's sleep and wait for Oberon.

(They sleep. Enter PUCK *who makes mischief with sleeping* BOTTOM*)*

OBERON
(*advancing*) I have some news. I'll make it swift.

PUCK
I'm all ears, boss (*miming donkey ears*) . . . you get my drift?

OBERON
Last night I met her in a clearing.

PUCK
Speak up my King, I'm hard of hearing. (*Laughing to himself*)

OBERON
I teased her 'bout her donkey friend.

PUCK
Teasing her is a joy without end.

OBERON
I didn't abate until she did . . .

PUCK
Until she gave you the servant kid?

OBERON
So now can set her free from this charm.

PUCK
And send this donkey back to the farm?

OBERON
You'll send him back to finish his play.
Just minus the ears . . .

PUCK
. . . and minus the hay.

OBERON

(Squeezing the potion into TITANIA'S *eyes)*

Wakey-wakey, fairy queen
Slept thee well . . .?

TITANIA
. . . I had a bad dream.

PUCK
Did you dream you loved a donkey chap?

TITANIA
Yes. How did you know . . .?

PUCK
. . . He's still on your lap.

(FAIRY enters)

TITANIA
He's a beast and a brute . . .

FAIRY
. . . That's what I've been saying
But your head was turned by his ears and his braying.

TITANIA
I still can't believe I would do such a thing.

FAIRY
Don't worry, my queen, it was only a fling.

OBERON
The dawn it breaks, and we must break now too.
And get ourselves polished for Theseus' do.

PUCK
I'll finish up with him, my dears
By taking off his old King Lears.[16]

OBERON
And wake the Greeks before we leave.
Their natural love they shall retrieve
And follow us the way we're heading
To attend a fancy triple wedding!

PUCK
When you wake forget last night
Everything will be alright.

FAIRY
Come, my queen, and on the route
(*To* OBERON) You can give us all a hoot

16—Another piece of Cockney rhyming slang that means ears

By telling us how she came to be found
With these mortals on the ground.

(Exeunt all. Horns blow from offstage. Enter THESEUS,
HIPPOLYTA, *and* EGEUS)

THESEUS
Now listen, unlike many punters[17]
We Greeks, my dear, are excellent hunters
Riding horses, jumping logs,
Firing arrows, barking dogs,
These are all the things you should
Have when you're hunting in a wood.

HIPPOLYTA
With Hercules, I once did ride,
Packs of wolves were by our side.
What a man . . . magnificent.

THESEUS
I don't think that's significant.
Just last week I killed a bear . . .

EGEUS
I don't remember . . .

THESEUS
. . . Who's that there?

EGEUS
My daughter, Hermia, lies in this here camp.

17—A term that can mean a customer or a client or a common folk

HIPPOLYTA
She must be wet, the ground is damp.

EGEUS
Lysander and Demetrius too?

HIPPOLYTA
I wonder what they've been up to.

EGEUS
And Helena, old Nedar's brat.

HIPPOLYTA
I'm sure they just came here to chat.

THESEUS
They clearly came to see me ride.
Why else would they have come outside?

HIPPOLYTA
And if I do remember well,
Today's the day that she must tell.
If she wants to do your bidding,
Or die a death . . .

EGEUS
 . . . I was just kidding.

THESEUS
Kidding or not, let's get them awake,
And make her choose, for goodness' sake.

> (*Horns and shouts offstage.* LYSANDER, DEMETRIUS,
> HELENA, *and* HERMIA *wake and start up*)

Good morrow, friends. A lovely day.
What brings you youngsters out this way?

LYSANDER
My Theseus, our plan is foiled.

HIPPOLYTA
And what a mess! Your clothes are soiled.

LYSANDER
We left the city to go and get wed.

EGEUS
I've heard enough; off with his head.

THESEUS
Let them finish . . . there's a good man!

DEMETRIUS
When Helena told me of their plan,
I followed them . . .

HELENA
. . . With me in tow.

DEMETRIUS
Around the wood we all did go
But as the night did turn to day,
My love for Herm did melt away
And waking now it's no surprise
I see only Helena's eyes.

HERMIA

I'm happy for you, and you're off my back.

HIPPOLYTA

I think you now can cut them some slack.

THESEUS

(*To* EGEUS) You're overruled. Her life is spared.

And back in town we'll all get paired.

You and him . . . (*Pointing to* HERMIA *and* LYSANDER)

HELENA

 . . . And me and you. (*Pointing to* DEMETRIUS)

HIPPOLYTA

Now that's the noble thing to do!

Let's go now and ready our bed.

THESEUS

Now that's just what the doctor said.

(*Exeunt* THESEUS, HIPPOLYTA, *and* EGEUS)

DEMETRIUS

Does anyone else feel kind of strange?

HERMIA

I feel myself but something's changed.

HELENA

Demetrius, you are really mine?

DEMETRIUS
I am until the end of time.

LYSANDER
And Hermia, you love me still?

HERMIA
If I can't have you, no one will.

LYSANDER
Are we awake . . .?

DEMETRIUS
 . . . I think so, yes.

HELENA
Well let's go and get our weddings blessed.

(Exeunt DEMETRIUS, LYSANDER, HELENA, *and* HERMIA)

BOTTOM

(Waking up)
Peter, Francis, Starveling, Snout!
I'm all alone. They're not about.
I had a dream here on the ground.
On my head, some ears I found.
And all the rest, you'd not believe.
The human brain could not conceive.
I'll find Quince now and spill the beans.
And find out what this vision means.
He'll turn it into a song and they
Will sing it at the end of our play!

(Exit BOTTOM)

SCENE II.

Athens. QUINCE'S *house.*

(Enter QUINCE, FLUTE, SNOUT, *and* STARVELING*)*

QUINCE
You've checked his house, good master Snout?

SNOUT
He wasn't there . . .

FLUTE
 . . . I bet he's out.

STARVELING
And if he doesn't come back today
We won't be putting on the play.

QUINCE
Without our Pyramus, we are toast.

FLUTE
And in all of Athens, he's the most.

QUINCE
The greatest guy and sweetest voice.

FLUTE
There's only him, we have no choice.

(Enter SNUG*)*

SNUG
And now the weddings are a few,
We could have made a bob[18] or two.

FLUTE
They would have paid a hefty sum
We could have retired . . .

QUINCE
. . . Oh, where is Bum?

(Enter BOTTOM*)*

BOTTOM
Alright my lads? Your Bottom's back.

QUINCE
You nearly gave me a heart attack!

STARVELING
Where are your ears . . .?

QUINCE
I guess they stopped growing.

BOTTOM
No more questions, we've got to be going.
The duke has dined, the couples are wed,
So grab your beards, and make the bed,
Go over your lines, and practice the dance.

18—British slang for a pound, money

Thisbe, make sure you've got clean underpants.
Clip your nails and sharpen your wits.
Brush your hair and straighten your kits.
No more jokes, no more deception.
Let us get to the reception.

(Exeunt all)

Act V

SCENE I.

Athens. The palace of THESEUS.

(Enter THESEUS, HIPPOLYTA, PUCK *as* PHILOSTRATE,
Lords, and Attendants)

HIPPOLYTA
The lovers' tales are magically curious.

THESEUS
To me, they all sound rather spurious.[19]
The young and in love are so befuddled.[20]
Testosterone[21] makes their brains all muddled.

HIPPOLYTA
Well, that's brought me back down to earth.

PHILOSTRATE
Here they come now in their laughter and mirth.

19—Not true or sincere
20—Confused
21—A chemical in the body associated with masculine qualities

(Enter LYSANDER, DEMETRIUS, HERMIA, *and* HELENA)

LYSANDER
Our hearts are dizzy . . .

DEMETRIUS
 . . . And our heads.

HERMIA
We're longing for our bridal beds.

THESEUS
You'll have to wait, we've got a show.
Philostrate booked it ages ago.

HELENA
Well that is ok. I like a good drama.
Remember the one 'bout the pig and the farmer?

PHILOSTRATE
Extraordinary piece, a work set apart.
But this one is more traditional art.

HIPPOLYTA
Traditional . . .? Meaning Roman or Greek?

PHILOSTRATE
Traditional dross, I had a quick peek.

THESEUS
Why did you book a bad act for my fest?

PHILOSTRATE
It's locals, non-actors, they're doing their best.

HIPPOLYTA
They made it for us, their cute little show?
Let's bring them on stage and give it a go.

PHILOSTRATE
For what you are about to see
Whatever it is . . . just don't blame me!

(A rather weak fanfare of trumpets. Enter QUINCE *and*
BOTTOM *for the Prologue)*

QUINCE
This epic work of daring . . .

BOTTOM
. . . Don't.

QUINCE
That's written here by Will . . .

BOTTOM
. . . Or won't.

QUINCE
It tells the tale of the beautiful . . .

BOTTOM
. . . Thisbe.

QUINCE
And how she found her long lost . . .

BOTTOM
. . . Frisbee.

QUINCE
We've got a lion, a wall . . .

BOTTOM
. . . A moon.

THESEUS
I hope this thing is starting soon.

BOTTOM
And now without no more . . .

QUINCE
. . . Delay
We'll show you all our brilliant . . .

BOTTOM
. . . Play!

(QUINCE *walks to the side of the stage and* BOTTOM *comes forward to the centre*)

BOTTOM AS PYRAMUS
The night is dark, there's not much light!
I should have met my love tonight.
The night is dark, the night is black,
I really want my Frisbee back.
The night is dark, the night is tall
I should have met her by this wall.
The night is dark, the night is hot,

I hope that she did not forgot.

SNOUT AS WALL

    (Lying on his back with his legs in the air)

The wall is here, the wall is here,
The wall is here, so have no fear.
If I put my legs like this,

        (Opening his legs)

You'll have a space for a little kiss.

BOTTOM AS PYRAMUS
The night is dark. I don't know how.
And "Frisbee" should be here by now.

FLUTE AS THISBE
Sorry all, I missed my cue.
My bladder's weak. I need the loo.

        *(*FLUTE *exits)*

QUINCE
(To the actors) He's gone to pee . . . just kill some time.

BOTTOM AS PYRAMUS
A little song . . . A little mime?

QUINCE
Just stand next to the hole in the wall,
She'll be back, no time at all.

BOTTOM AS PYRAMUS
The night is dark, the night is long,
I wonder where my Frisbee's gone.

SNOUT AS WALL
She's in the loo . . .

BOTTOM AS PYRAMUS
 . . . I'm acting here.

HELENA
This show is bad . . .

DEMETRIUS
 . . . Be quiet, my dear.

FLUTE AS THISBE
I'm back. There is no toilet paper.

QUINCE
Just get on stage. We'll deal with it later.
Remember now, you're Pyramus's miss,
So stand by the wall and prepare for the kiss.

FLUTE AS THISBE
My lips are red, I'm feeling frisky.
I think this scene could get a bit risky.

BOTTOM AS PYRAMUS
The night is dark, the night is queer,
You know we're only acting here?

FLUTE AS THISBE
You'll be my man; I'll be your toy.
Now pucker up, you naughty boy!

SNOUT AS WALL
Please hurry up, my legs are sore.

QUINCE
Bottom, what you waiting for?

BOTTOM AS PYRAMUS
The night is dark, the night is gloom
Come kiss me now on Ninny's tomb.

FLUTE AS THISBE
Sounds kinky, baby. Show me where.

BOTTOM AS PYRAMUS
It's off the stage . . . I'm going there.

(Exeunt BOTTOM *and* FLUTE*)*

SNOUT AS WALL
I'm going too, my legs to rub
And then I'm going down the pub.

(Exit SNOUT)

HERMIA
Is that the end . . . ?

LYSANDER
. . . I'm really not sure.

QUINCE
Please do not fret, we've got some more.

(Enter SNUG *and* STARVELING*)*

SNUG AS LION
I am the lion, but don't have a fit.
I'm Snug, the joiner, in a lion kit.
My mane is fake, my claws are too.
I made them at home from paper and glue.

STARVELING AS MOON
I am the moon, I am the moon,
I am the moon, I am the moon,
I am the moon, I am the moon.
I hope that Thisbe back on soon.
I am the moon, I am the moon.

(Enter FLUTE*)*

FLUTE AS THISBE
Is the place of 'Ninny's' tomb?

SNUG AS LION
This is where I do the roar,
The thing that I explained before . . .

(He roars and FLUTE *runs off dropping a scarf)*

SNUG AS LION
You dropped your scarf. I'll make it gory.
I'm doing this as part of the story.

(SNUG *shakes* FLUTE'S *scarf and exits*)

QUINCE
Well done, Snug. Now leave it and go.
We've arrived at the climax of the show.

(Enter BOTTOM*)*

BOTTOM AS PYRAMUS
The night is dark, but now a bit less.

STARVELING AS MOON
Cos I am here . . .

BOTTOM AS PYRAMUS
. . . What is this mess?

STARVELING AS MOON
I am the moon . . .

BOTTOM AS PYRAMUS
. . . I know you're not lyin'.
Was Thisbe eaten by a lion?

STARVELING AS MOON
Well I'm not quite sure 100%,
But I think that that's the way it went.

BOTTOM AS PYRAMUS
The night was dark, and now it's black
Cos Thisbe was a lion's snack.
Now there's nothing left to do
But kill myself . . .

THESEUS
. . . Oh please . . . please do!

STARVELING AS MOON
Here use this . . . *(hands* BOTTOM *a knife)*

BOTTOM AS PYRAMUS
. . . Well thank you, friend
And now for my dramatic end . . .

(Stabs himself)

The night is dark . . .

QUINCE
. . . get on with it.

BOTTOM AS PYRAMUS
This is the dramatic bit.
I was fine, but now I'm not.
Thisbe's gone and she was hot.
I'll miss her hair and little beard.
Now it's time I disappeared.

(Dies. Recovers briefly)

The night was dark . . . *(Dies again)*

STARVELING AS MOON
. . . I'm off! You're dead!

(STARVELING exits, FLUTE *enters)*

FLUTE AS THISBE
. . . Where's my little pyramid?

Oh woe is me, I'm all alone.

HERMIA
I wish you were. Let's all go home!

QUINCE
Get on with it . . .

FLUTE AS THISBE
 . . . You're like a log
But before I go, let's have a snog.[22]

BOTTOM
Nice try, but not alive or dead.

FLUTE AS THISBE
So time to hit my final bed

(Takes knife from next to BOTTOM *and stabs herself)*

I leave you now in deep distress.
And I hope you all did like this dress.

(Dies)

THESEUS
Just Moonshine and Lion survive the death.

HERMIA
The wall hasn't taken yet his final breath.

BOTTOM
(Sitting up) I assure you; it's over . . .

22—A kiss

HELENA
. . . Thank goodness for that.

BOTTOM
Just the last song, then we'll pass round the hat.

THESEUS
Don't worry 'bout the final bit.
That's the way I look at it.

HIPPOLYTA
Well said, my dear, a great review.
I have to say I share your view.

THESEUS
Goodbye, my lads, and no encore.
Just turn around and head for the door.
Philostrate! That was seriously dire!

PHILOSTRATE
Don't say I didn't warn you, sire.

DEMETRIUS
But now it's over, can we go?

LYSANDER
Upstairs to start the . . . well, you know!

THESEUS
Before the fairies come to muddle,
To bed, to sleep . . . maybe a cuddle?

HIPPOLYTA
Like I told you before, nothing so gory.
But if you're really good I might read you a story.

(Exeunt everyone except PHILOSTRATE *who becomes* PUCK*)*

PUCK
And no more human form I'll take
And no more magic will I make
Now they've heard the wedding bells
I'll put away my little spells.
In fact, I'll guard this house tonight
To make sure that they sleep all right.
... Or whatever they do in those rooms upstairs
After brushing their teeth and saying their prayers.

(Enter OBERON *and* TITANIA *with their train)*

OBERON
All you fairies bless this house,
And all you beasts from cat to mouse,
Keep your chasing pawsies soft
And don't disturb the sleeping loft.

TITANIA
All our lovers now are hitched,[23]
Their single lives forever ditched.
We wish them all a life of joy
(To OBERON*)* and I haven't forgotten the servant boy.

23—Married

OBERON

Oh, let it go I do beseech
This here is my final speech!
Let their lives be clean, not grubby.
Let their kids be fun and chubby.
Let the women wear the pants.
And let men learn how to dance.
And let the fairies all agree
To let them live accordingly!

(Exeunt OBERON, TITANIA, *and train)*

PUCK

If you're feeling all offended
Cos this play we have amended
Just forget that you were here
And none of us we did appear.
Cos that's the point, the gist, the theme,
We're all just fairies in a dream.
So go home and don't reprehend:
And soon you'll feel you're on the mend.
Just keep a little thought of Puck,
And if you do, I'll bring you luck.
From the tips of my toes to the tip of my tongue,
I'll cast you my shadow and my shadow is long;
If you're feeling all playful, just give me a call;
And some fun like tonight I will share with all.
And if all of these couplets didn't make us good friends,
I will visit you later and make my
... amends.

More Drama Resources from Alphabet Publishing

Silly Shakespeare for Students by Paul Leonard Murray

Macbeth

Pericles

Short Original Plays by Alice Savage

Just Desserts: A foodie drama about a chef gone bad

Introducing Rob: Lola's family loves her new boyfriend. Until they actually meet him

Colorado Ghost Story: Two exchange students get into trouble in the old West

Strange Medicine: Who decides what the truth is?

The Drama Book: Lesson Plans, Activities, and Scripts for the English Language Classroom by Alice Savage

ISTD Coursebooks by Alice Savage

The Integrated Skills Through Drama coursebooks contain a complete curriculum built around an original one-act play. Aimed at intermediate learners, teenagers and older.

Her Own Worst Enemy: A serious comedy about choosing a major

Only the Best Intentions: A love triangle between a guy, a girl and a game

Rising Water: A stormy drama about what happens to people in a crisis

Alphabet Publishing is an independent publisher of creative and innovative educational material. All of our resources were conceived and created by teachers working in the classroom. We support our creators by giving them creative control and by sharing profits. Learn more about us and our resources at www.alphabetpublish.com

Printed in Great Britain
by Amazon